KINDERGARTEN

Illustrations by Michele Ackerman, Marie Allen, Martha Avilés, Tiphanie Beeke, Michelle Berg, Tim Ellis, Louise Gardner, Kallen Godsey, Barbara Lanza, Lindsey McCool, Michael Miller, Kathy Mitchell, Robin Moro, Chris Moroney, Sherry Neidigh, Burgandy Nilles, Ryan Sias, Susan Spellman, Jeremy Tugeau, George Ulrich, Ted Williams, David Wojtowycz, and Maria Woods

Photography by Shutterstock, ImageClub, PhotoDisc, Jupiter Images Unlimited, Art Explosion, IStock, Artville, Siede Preis Photography, and Brian Warling Photography

Louis Weber, C.E.O.
Publications International, Ltd.

7373 North Cicero Avenue
Lincolnwood, Illinois 60712

Ground Floor, 59 Gloucester Place
London W1U 8JJ

Customer Service: 1-800-595-8484 or customer_service@pilbooks.com

www.pilbooks.com

p i kids is a trademark of Publications International, Ltd., and is registered in the United States.
Brain Games is a trademark of Publications International, Ltd.

8 7 6 5 4 3 2 1

Manufactured in China.

ISBN-10: 1-4508-3254-7
ISBN-13: 978-1-4508-3254-0

 publications international, ltd.

Letter to Parents

Welcome to Brain Games!

Get ready for an exciting kind of early-learning activity! These 301 questions tackle key benchmarks across core categories such as language arts and math, as well as science, social sciences, physical and emotional development, fine arts, and foreign language. Categories are scattered throughout the book, and questions progress from easy to hard for a graduated learning experience. Colorful illustrations and photography help to present the material in a fun and engaging way. Answer keys for all questions are located in the last section of the book. Settle down, open the book, and have fun learning with your child today.

How to Use

- Open to the desired set of questions.

- Read the questions aloud. Ask your child to point to or name the answer.

- Answer keys are at the back of the book

Some Tips

- Your child might not be familiar with all of the content on these pages. Take the time to introduce new concepts and characters when these kinds of questions come up.

- Encourage your child to use the book with friends and/or siblings, too. Take turns asking each other the questions. The material might serve as a good review for older children!

- Be positive and encouraging. Learning should be fun! When your child seems tired, frustrated, or unfocused, take a break. You can always play again later.

Questions

For solutions, turn to page 98.

Which animal lives in the desert?

How many ladybugs?

What is this picture? What is its first letter?

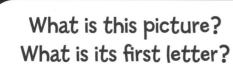

_ed

Do you brush your teeth before or after you go to bed?

Questions

Put these pictures in the right order.

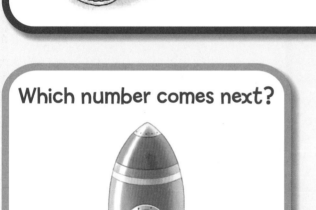

Which number comes next?

3 __ 1

Match the uppercase letter with the lowercase letter.

d   E

e   F

f   D

Questions

For solutions, turn to page 100.

Which animal lives underwater?

How many flowers?

Which of these vehicles begins with the letter V?

Which sign shows the number twelve?

Questions

Which uppercase and lowercase letters are missing?

Starting at the left, which person is fifth in line?

How many words in this sentence start with the letter **B**?

My best buddy Bob missed the bus to the big baseball game, so he ran back home and biked his way over.

Questions

For solutions, turn to page 102.

Starting from the left, which fish is third?

Which letters are missing?

Put these pictures in the right order.

For solutions, turn to page 103.

Questions

How many fruits do you see during snack time?

How many party hats are in this picture?

Questions

For solutions, turn to page 104.

Do you eat dinner before or after school?

What is this picture? What is its first letter?

_ake

Which number comes next?

15 16 ___

Which of these animals begins with the letter **c**?

Questions

How many umbrellas are in this picture?

Can you name all the things in this picture that start with the letter **B**?

Questions

For solutions, turn to page 106.

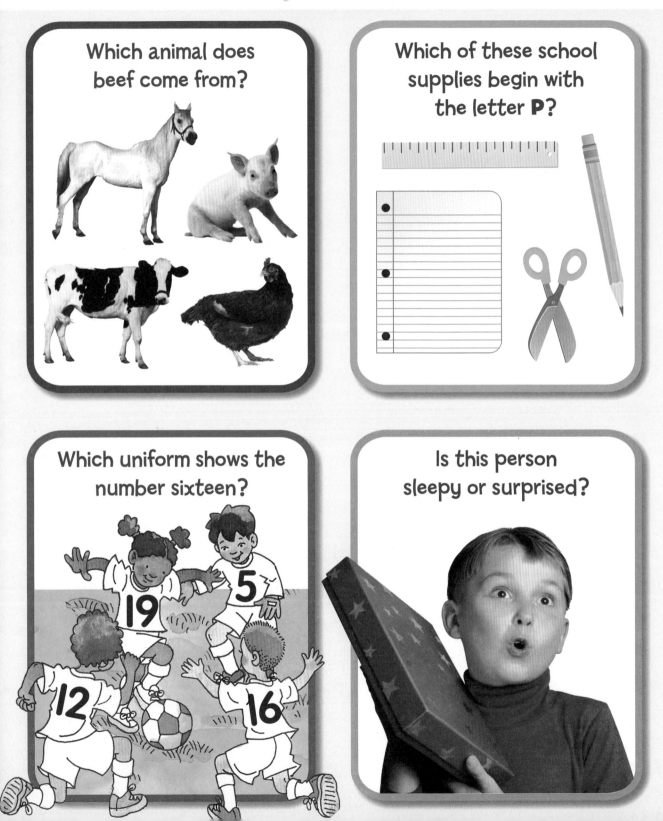

Which animal does beef come from?

Which of these school supplies begin with the letter **P**?

Which uniform shows the number sixteen?

Is this person sleepy or surprised?

Questions

How many things are brown?

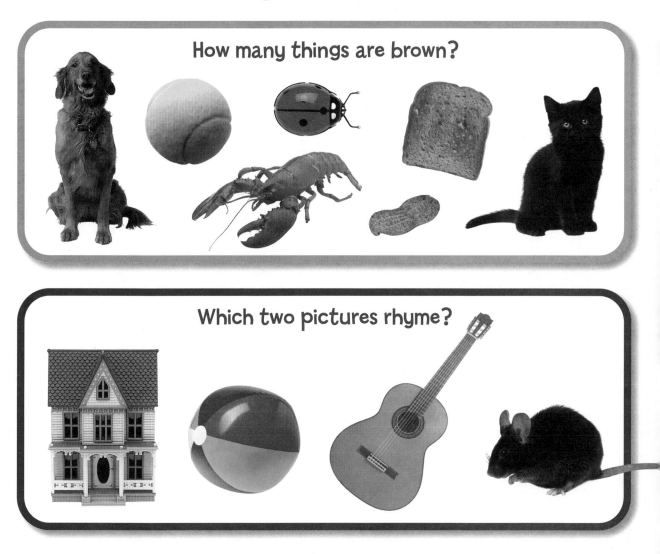

Which two pictures rhyme?

How many words in this sentence start with the letter S?

While we were at the seashore last Sunday, we stopped swimming to skip along the beach and collect shells that had washed up on the sand.

Questions

For solutions, turn to page 108.

Which building is on the right?

How many things in this picture start with the letter **W**?

How many things that start with the letter **J** is the clown juggling?

Count 1 back from 20. What do you get?

Questions

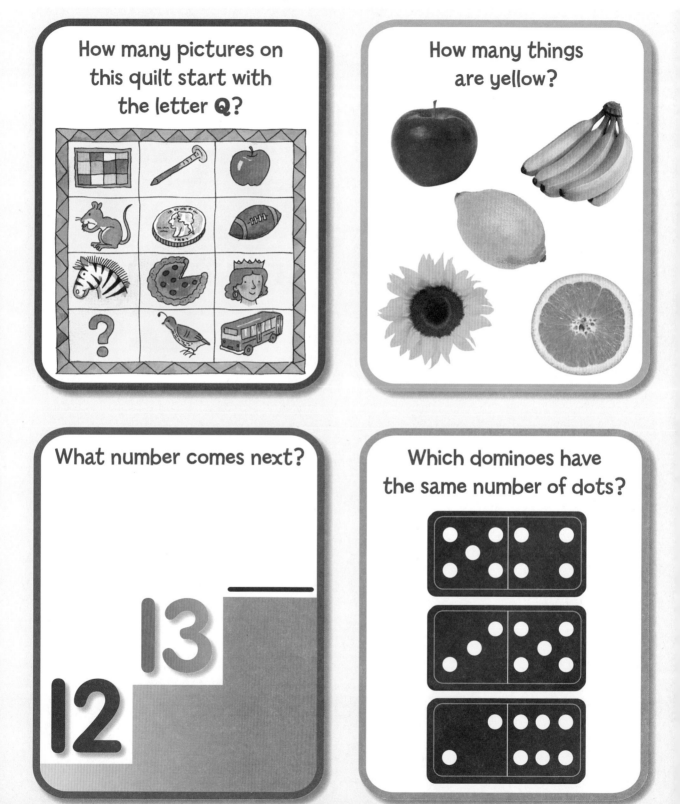

How many pictures on this quilt start with the letter **Q**?

How many things are yellow?

What number comes next?

Which dominoes have the same number of dots?

Questions

For solutions, turn to page 110.

How many things in this nest start with the letter **N**?

What does the Spanish word "si" mean?

yes

no

hello

How many things in this picture start with the letter **S**?

Questions

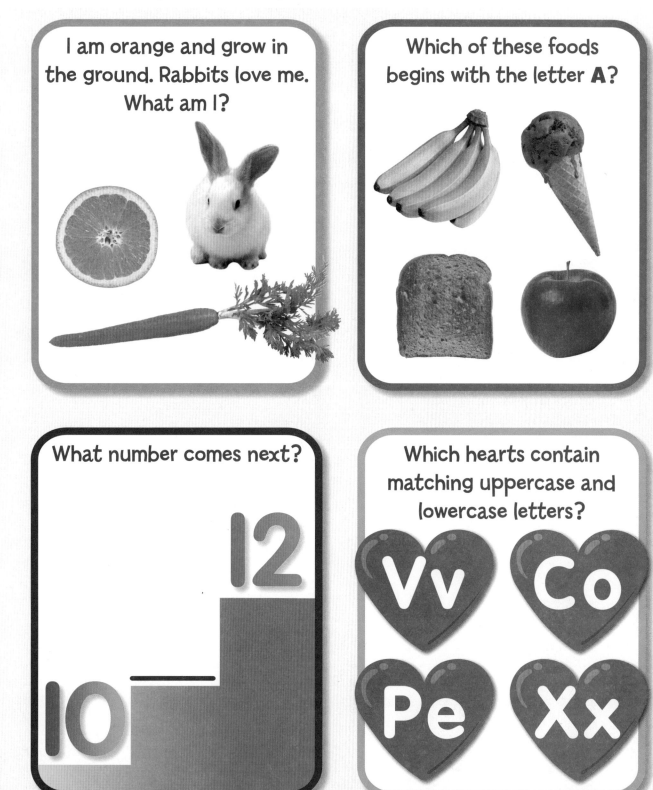

I am orange and grow in the ground. Rabbits love me. What am I?

Which of these foods begins with the letter **A**?

What number comes next?

12

10

Which hearts contain matching uppercase and lowercase letters?

Vv

Co

Pe

Xx

Questions

For solutions, turn to page 112.

I have wrinkly skin and a hard shell,
and I hatch from an egg. Which animal am I?

Put these pictures in
the right order.

Follow the path with
the pictures that start
with the letter **F**.

Start

Finish

Questions

How many monkeys are in this picture?

Point to all the things in this picture that start with F.

What month is Presidents' Day in?

April
February
June
October

Which two pictures rhyme?

Match the animal to the tracks it made.

Which one is used to put out fires?

Match the lowercase stamp to the uppercase letter.

g   N ☐

n   H ☐

h   G ☐

How many words in this sentence start with the letter **Q**?

The quality of the queen's quilt was quite good for the price of one shiny quarter.

Which group has fewer?

What is this picture? What is its first letter?

_uitar

Questions

For solutions, turn to page 116.

Which ball contains matching uppercase and lowercase letters?

Qq Bd

Mn Yp

What is this picture? What is its first letter?

__ion

Count 2 back from 10. What do you get?

10 9

What does the Spanish word "gracias" mean?

please

what

thank you

For solutions, turn to page 117.

Questions

Which of these things begins with the letter T?

Count the rubber ducks.

How many things in this picture start with the letter D?

Questions

For solutions, turn to page 118.

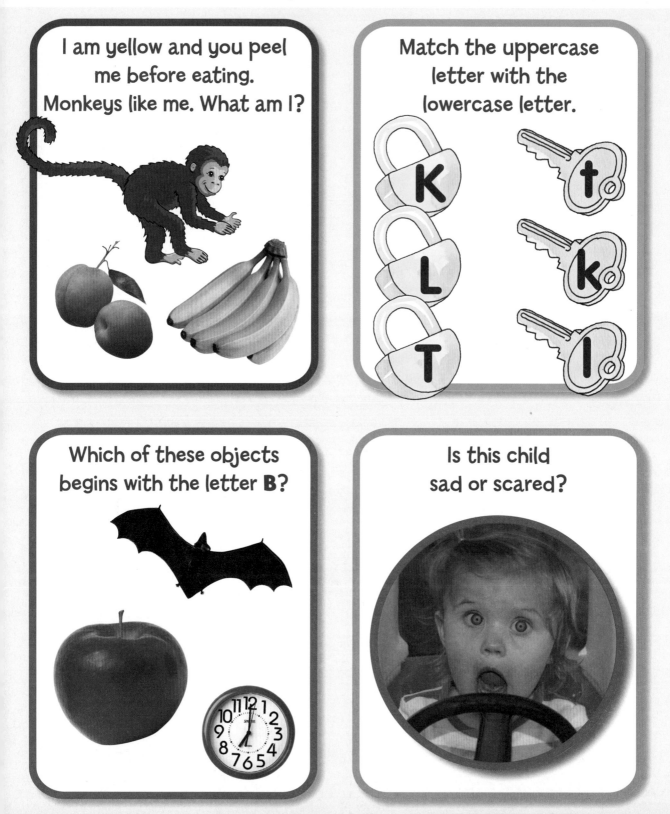

I am yellow and you peel me before eating. Monkeys like me. What am I?

Match the uppercase letter with the lowercase letter.

Which of these objects begins with the letter **B**?

Is this child sad or scared?

Questions

Put these pictures in the right order.

Which of these toys begins with the letter **y**?

What is this picture? What is its first letter?

_ig

Questions

For solutions, turn to page 120.

What number comes next?

8 9 ___

Match the uppercase letter with the lowercase letter.

G   y

R   g

Y   r

Point to all the things in this picture that start with the letter **C**.

Questions

Which of these things begin with the letter **K**?

Which animal crossed the finish line first?

Which of these clothes begins with the letter **G**?

I have sharp teeth, scaly skin, and can swim in water or walk on land. Which am I?

Questions

For solutions, turn to page 122.

How many yellow flowers?

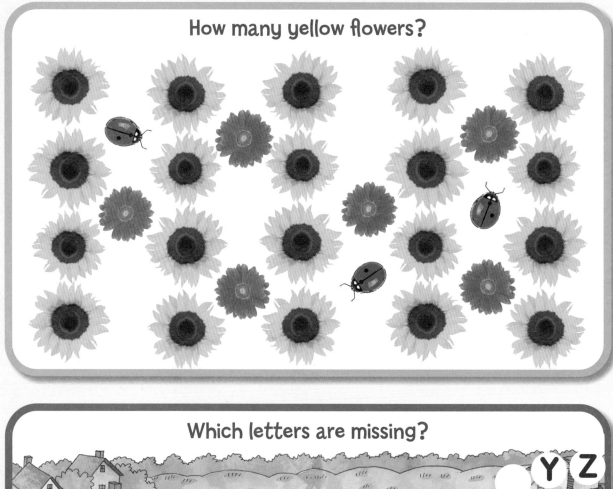

Which letters are missing?

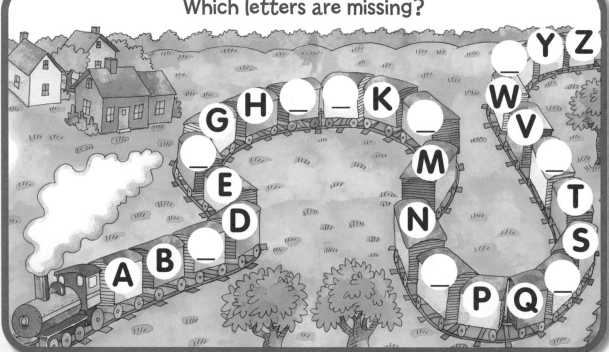

Questions

Are there more seashells or shovels?

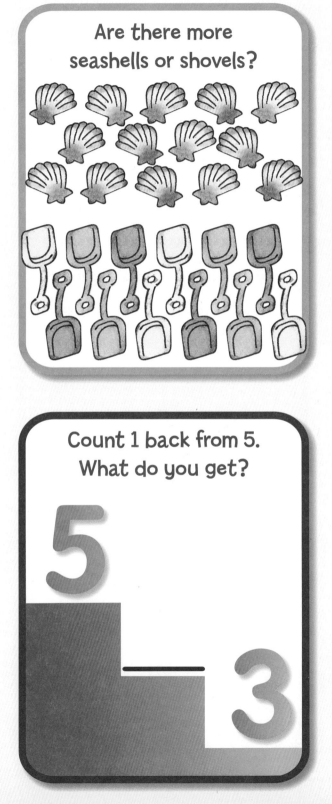

I live in Africa, have stripes, and am part of the horse family. Which animal am I?

Count 1 back from 5. What do you get?

5 ___ 3

Which two pictures rhyme?

Questions

For solutions, turn to page 124.

Put these pictures in the right order.

Count the tigers. Which word tells how many?

Six   Seven

What color are most of the leaves on this tree?

For solutions, turn to page 125.

Questions

Which bugs have the same number of legs?

Which sign is an octagon?

STOP

Which pictures on the front page of the paper start with the letter P?

What does the Spanish word "adios" mean?

welcome

good-bye

hello

Questions

For solutions, turn to page 126.

How many things in this picture start with the letter **L**?

Which ice-cream cones contain matching uppercase and lowercase letters?

Question

Find all the hidden **Z** words at the zoo.

Questions

For solutions, turn to page 128.

Which pizza is divided equally into two halves?

Which of these things begins with the letter X?

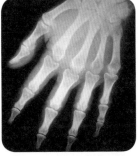

You have four apples. Your mom gives you one more. How many do you have?

For solutions, turn to page 129.

Questions

What does the Spanish word "hola" mean?

hot

help

hello

What do you wear to stay safe while biking?

Match the uppercase and lowercase letters.

Questions

For solutions, turn to page 130.

How many apples do you see in this picture?

Point to the things a plant needs to grow.

You have four jelly beans.
You eat two.
How many do you have left?

$-$ $=$

For solution, turn to page 131.

Question

How many things are green?

Questions

For solutions, turn to page 132.

Which fireman will be second down the pole?

How many pairs do you see?

What is this picture? What is its first letter?

_ish

Which two pictures rhyme?

For solutions, turn to page 133.

Questions

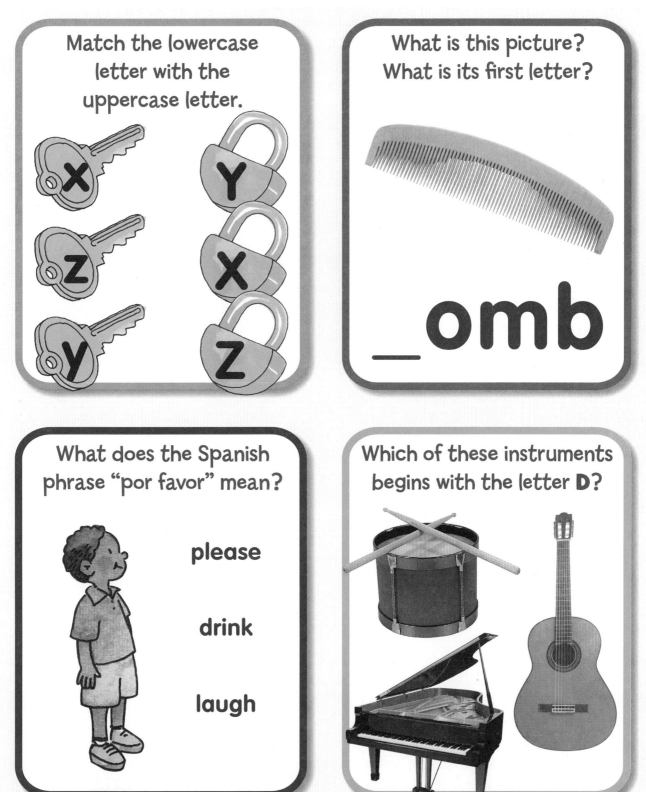

Match the lowercase letter with the uppercase letter.

What is this picture? What is its first letter?

__omb

What does the Spanish phrase "por favor" mean?

please

drink

laugh

Which of these instruments begins with the letter D?

Questions

For solutions, turn to page 134.

Count the parrots. Which word tells how many?

Seven   Eight

How many things are purple?

Read the poem, then find the rhyming words in the picture.

I have a cat
who sits on a mat.
He ate cookies and cake
in the sand by the lake.
He liked to lie in the sun;
now he's so big, he can't even run.

For solutions, turn to page 135.

Questions

Which person is on the right?

Finish the pattern.

day, night,

day, night,

day, _____

How many circles?

There are five fish in the aquarium. You add three more. How many are there?

Questions

For solutions, turn to page 136.

Choose the picture that rhymes with the underlined word.

The **duck** flew over the_____.

Which word in this sentence should have a capital letter?

bobby likes chocolate cupcakes.

There are seven frogs. Two of them hop away. How many are left?

Which tool would you use to see things up close?

Questions

Which suitcase is full?

Which one doesn't belong?

What shape is the planet Earth?

cube   cylinder   sphere

What does the French word "oui" mean?

yes

no

hello

Questions

For solutions, turn to page 138.

One sock is missing its mate. Which pattern is missing?

Put the letters together. What word is this?

B + E + E

What do you get when you mix **yellow** and **red**?

Uniform starts with a long **U** sound. Which person is wearing a uniform?

Questions

Counting backward, which number is missing?

8   7   6   4

Which of these is not a rectangle?

Which animal rhymes with chair?

Questions

for solutions turn to page 140

Are there more horses inside or outside the pen?

Which person is last in line for a turn on the slide?

For solutions, turn to page 141.

Questions

What part of the boat is a triangle?

Which tool measures time?

Can you find 5 things wrong in this picture?

Questions

For solutions, turn to page 142.

Which letter is missing?
Use the picture
to help you decide.

b___s

Put the letters together.
What word is this?

S + U + N

Which dinosaur is biggest?

Which ball gets tossed
through the hoop?

Questions

Read the sentence. Choose the picture
that rhymes with the underlined word.

I tried to feed the **<u>goat</u>** some corn, but it ate my hat instead.

Which group has
more animals?

What did the cow
jump over?

sun

moon

star

Questions

For solutions, turn to page 144.

Which object is in the middle?

Which letter is missing? Use the picture to help you decide.

d___g

Which animal is in front of the barn?

Which animal is the chick's mother?

For solutions, turn to page 145.

Questions

What flavor comes next? Cherry or mint?

What do you get when you mix **red** and **blue**?

Which one rhymes with clock?

Questions

For solutions, turn to page 146.

There are ten bees. Four of them return to the hive.
How many are left?

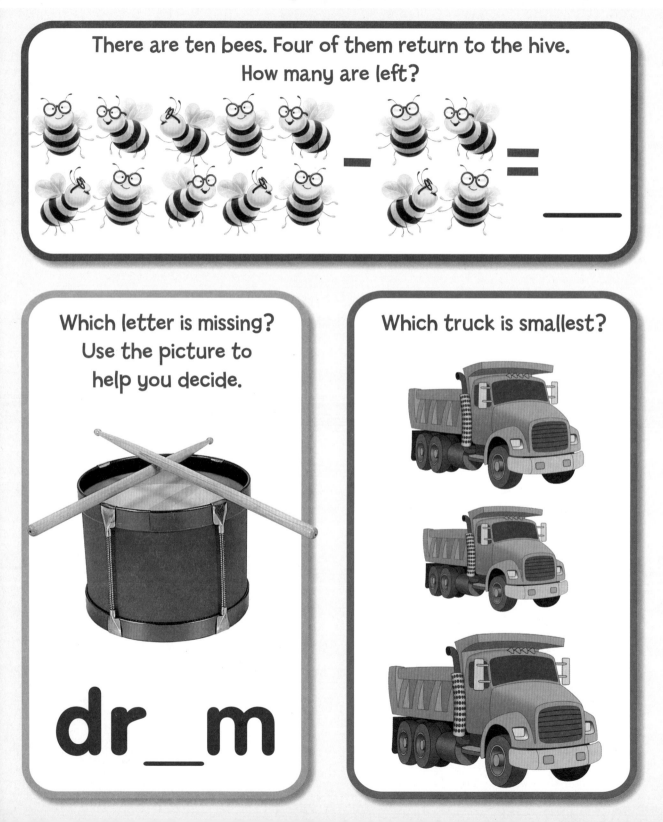

Which letter is missing?
Use the picture to
help you decide.

Which truck is smallest?

dr_m

Questions

Which words should have capital letters?

my good friend annie is moving to a new home by the ocean in california.

Fill in the missing letter.

bea__

What is another word for an uppercase letter? It starts with this letter.

C

_____

What do you get when you mix **white** and **red**?

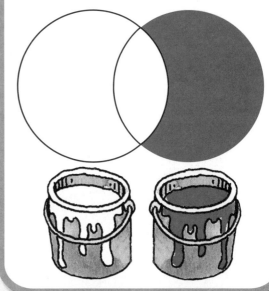

Questions

For solutions, turn to page 148.

Which president is on the dollar bill?

Which rabbit is above the ground?

Questions

Which animal's name starts with a vowel?

Is the person who flies an airplane called a pilot or a pirate?

Which shelf are the triangles on?

top

middle

bottom

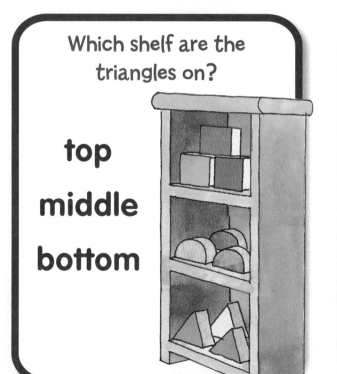

Change the first letter in "see" to get a flying insect. What letter did you use?

_ee

Questions

For solutions, turn to page 150.

Which color comes next?

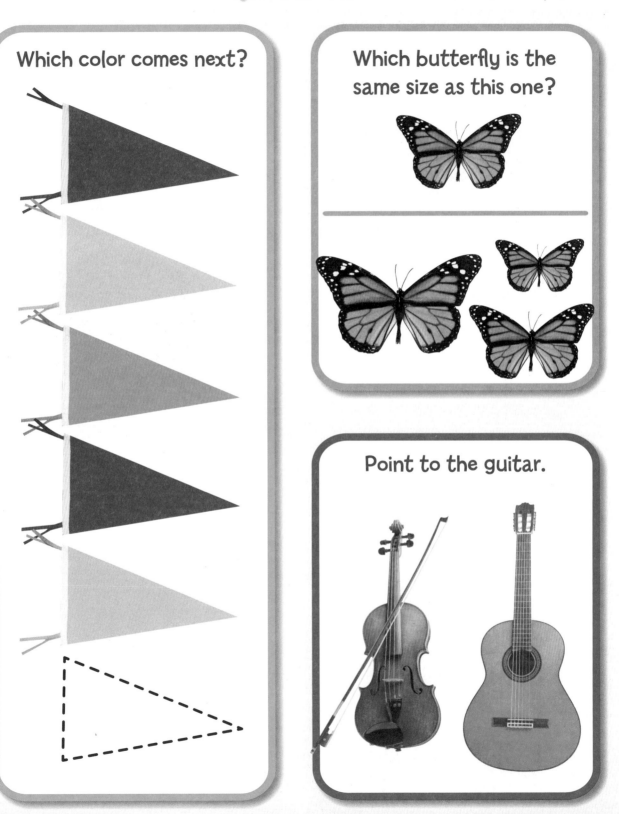

Which butterfly is the same size as this one?

Point to the guitar.

Questions

How many words in this sentence start with **G**?

The silly goose giggled at the giant swan.

Which of these is not a triangle?

Put the letters together. What word is this?

C + A + T

Fill in the missing letter.

skun_

Questions

For solutions, turn to page 152.

What kind of little animal did Mary have?

piglet

kitten

lamb

calf

Which object is heaviest?

Which season comes after spring?

fall

summer

winter

Questions

Point to the girl's elbows.

Fill in the blank.
The children are playing
Duck, _____, Goose.

Which words should have
capital letters?

it was a good idea to let
john play. he helped us
win the game!

What color comes next?

Questions

For solutions, turn to page 154.

Point to the musical instrument.

What did Hansel drop on the ground to make a trail?

bread crumbs

buttons

string

Which duck is below the boat?

Questions

Which one doesn't belong?

Which thing rhymes with coat?

Put the letters together. What word is this?

P + I + G

Which giraffe is tallest?

Questions

For solutions, turn to page 156.

Change the first letter in "map" to get a kind of hat. What letter did you use?

_ap

Put the letters together. What word is this?

N + E + T

What did Humpty Dumpty have a great fall off of?

What month is it if we're watching fireworks for Independence Day?

June

July

August

September

Questions

Which rock has fewer turtles?

You've made five ice-cream cones for your friends.
Three more friends come over and you make cones for them.
How many ice-cream cones have you made?

What did Jack trade his old cow for?

wagon

beans

new cow

Questions

For solutions, turn to page 158.

How many states are there in the USA?

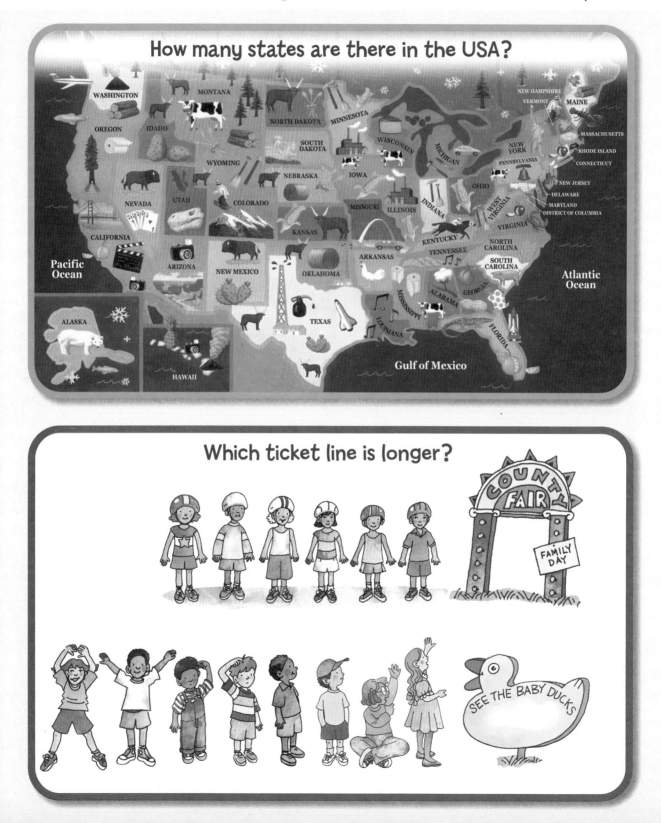

Which ticket line is longer?

Questions

Which letter is missing?
Use the picture to
help you decide.

sh___ll

Which words should have
capital letters?

on mondays we have art.

Choose the picture
that rhymes with the
underlined word.

The black **bat** flew
by the scared _____.

Which letter is missing?
Use the pictures to
help you decide.

m

c

n

p

Questions

For solutions, turn to page 160.

How many times do you see this pattern  in this picture?

What did Rapunzel let down?

hair

rope

vine

Questions

Which building is the fire station?

Which rabbits are next to each other?

In *The Tortoise and the Hare,*
who won the race by going slow and steady?

tortoise

hare

snail

Questions

For solutions, turn to page 162.

Put the letters together.
What word is this?

D + O + G

When someone gives you a
present, do you feel
angry or happy?

How many squares?

Which planet's name
starts with **S**?

Saturn

Mercury   **Jupiter**

Change the first letter in "cat" to get a flying animal. What letter did you use?

_at

What do you get when you mix **blue** and **yellow**?

What do you call your parents' parents?

Which one does a car need to run?

Questions

For solutions, turn to page 164.

Which animal is the horse's baby?

Which whale is under the water?

Where will this bus take the children every morning?

store

school

library

Questions

There are two nests with eggs. One nest has seven eggs. The other has four. How many eggs are there?

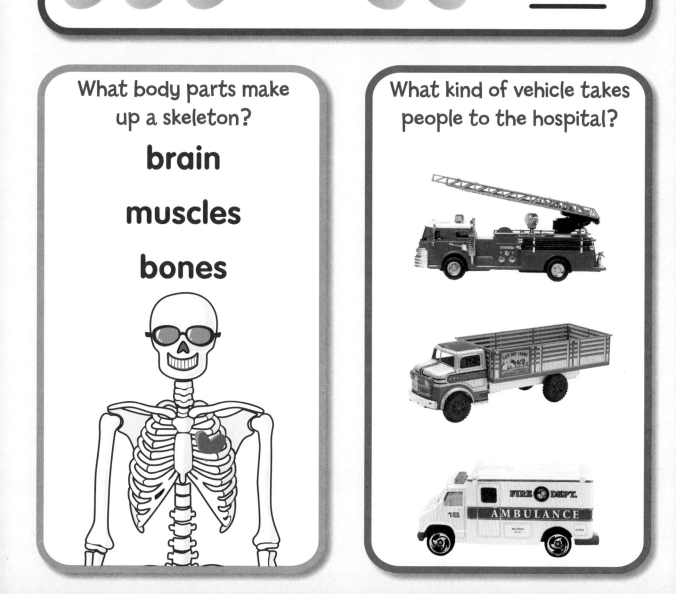

What body parts make up a skeleton?

brain

muscles

bones

What kind of vehicle takes people to the hospital?

Questions

For solutions, turn to page 166.

Which one would you use to stay dry?

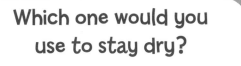

Which letter do you hear at the end of **fork**?

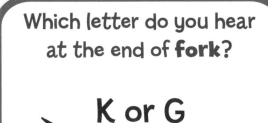

K or G

Which food's name starts with a consonant?

How many words in this sentence start with **M**?

The messy monkeys had a mop.

Questions

Does the red light mean stop or go?

Which letter do you hear at the end of **leaf**?

D or F

Fill in the blank to find a shorter way to say this sentence.

You and I like apples.

_____ like apples.

They

It

We

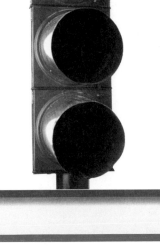

Point to the musical instrument.

Questions

For solutions, turn to page 168.

What did Rumpelstiltskin spin into gold?

yarn   **straw**   **corn**

Which activity takes longer — climbing a mountain or a ladder?

Which tool helps you see in the dark?

For solution, turn to page 169.

Question

Which items have a hard C sound like you hear in the word "car"?

Questions

For solutions, turn to page 170.

What is another way to say "action word"?

noun

verb

adjective

Which tool can be used to measure temperature?

What is this mark?

exclamation point

comma

question mark

In an emergency, what number do you dial for help?

411

911

800

For solutions, turn to page 171.

Questions

Which word means "person, place, or thing"?

noun

adjective

adverb

What time is it?

2:00 11:00 4:00

Which activity takes longer — reading a book or a sign?

EXIT

What word should go on this red sign?

SLOW **STOP** **GO**

Questions

For solutions, turn to page 172.

Look at the clues. Put them together. What is the word?

Which one would you find in **Paris**?

What does a person need to put on before going out into the sun?

Sunscreen Lotion

For solutions, turn to page 173.

Questions

Which words have the soft **C** sound?

Cindy ate cereal in the center of her city.

How much is this worth?

Which picture shows something frozen?

Point to the buildings in order from shortest to tallest.

Question

For solution, turn to page 174.

Which pictures have a long **A**
like you hear in the word "game"?
Follow those pictures from start to finish.

For solutions, turn to page 175.

Questions

Fill in the blank to find a shorter way to say this sentence.

The girl is skating.

_____ is skating.

He

She

It

What's missing from this bird?

Which pictures have a long **I** like you hear in the word "ice"?

Use the picture to answer the riddle.

What can you put in a bucket to make it lighter?

Questions

For solutions, turn to page 176.

How much are one penny and one dime worth?

What do you say when you want someone to pass the pizza?

please / you're welcome

Use the picture to answer the riddle.

What falls in winter but never gets hurt?

Point to the cube.

Question

How many things in this picture have the short **O** sound you hear in the word "octopus"?

Questions

For solutions, turn to page 178.

Which person is oldest?

What does an audience do at the end of a performance?

What mark do you put at the end of a regular sentence?

period •

comma ,

question mark ?

Point to the twins.

Questions

What's missing from this van?

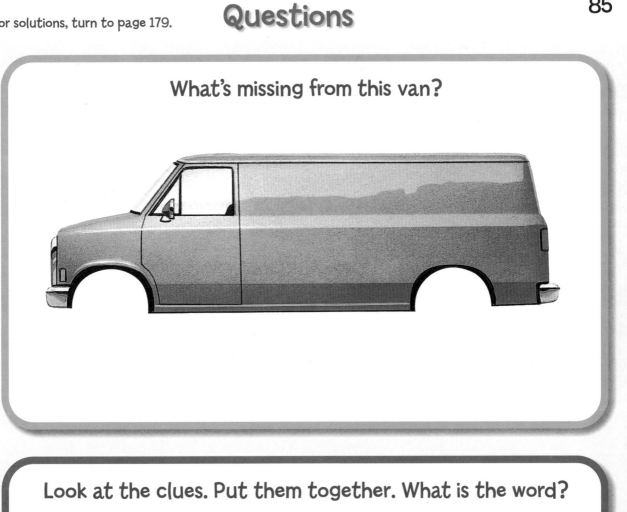

Look at the clues. Put them together. What is the word?

Questions

For solutions, turn to page 180.

Fill in the blank to find a shorter way to say this sentence.

The children are making music.

_____ are making music.

They

Them

It

Which one is the cylinder?

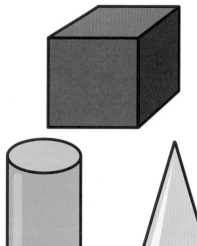

How many of these things are alive?

How many months are there in a year?

20

12

8

10

Questions

Which day comes before Monday?

Friday **Sunday** **Tuesday**

Which meal is better for you?

What time is it?

1:00   12:00   9:00

Questions

For solutions, turn to page 182.

Name the 5 senses.

_____

_____

_____

_____

_____

How many of these things can you recycle?

Questions

Look at the clues. Put them together. What is the word?

Which pictures have a long **o** like you hear in the word "boat"?

Questions

For solutions, turn to page 184.

Which one doesn't belong?

Point to the plant's roots.

Which item can you buy with two dimes?

20¢

35¢

Which word in this sentence describes something?

Jack picked a pretty flower.

What happens second?

What body part is the squirrel missing?

What is the better one to say when you need to get by someone?

excuse me / I'm sorry

Questions

For solutions, turn to page 186.

Which pictures start with a soft **G** like the word "gym"?

What is the opposite of wet?

dry

hot

sticky

Which picture shows a windy day?

What time is it?

9:00   11:00   7:00

For solutions, turn to page 187.

Questions

Which pictures have a short **E** like you hear in the word "bed"?

Is California on the east or west coast of the United States?

Questions

For solutions, turn to page 188.

Put these events in order.

Point to the sphere.

Which group of coins has the same value as one quarter?

Questions

Which item costs more?

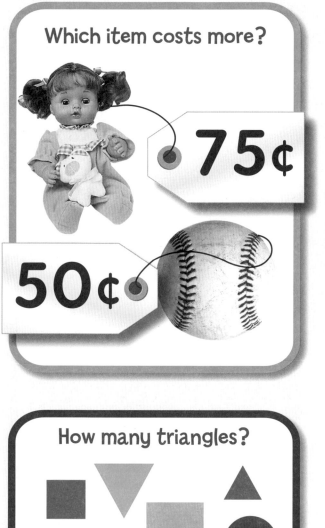

75¢

50¢

Which day comes after Thursday?

Monday
Wednesday
Friday
Sunday

How many triangles?

Put the letters together. What word is this?

P + I + G

Questions

For solutions, turn to page 190.

Which of these pictures have a hard **G** as in "girl"?

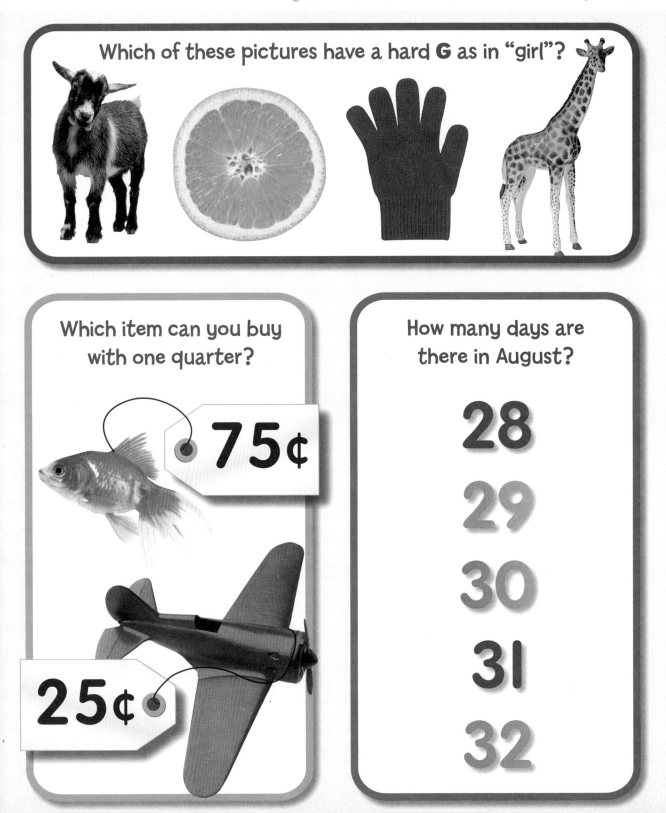

Which item can you buy with one quarter?

75¢

25¢

How many days are there in August?

28

29

30

31

32

For solutions, turn to page 191.

Questions

Can you buy this item with two quarters?

$1.00

You have twelve toy soldiers. You give a friend six.
How many do you have left?

___ - ___ = ___

Which animal lives
in the desert?

camel

How many ladybugs?

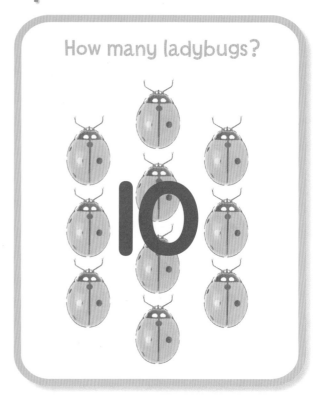

What is this picture?
What is its first letter?

bed

Do you brush your
teeth before or after
you go to bed?

Answers for page 5

Put these pictures in the right order.

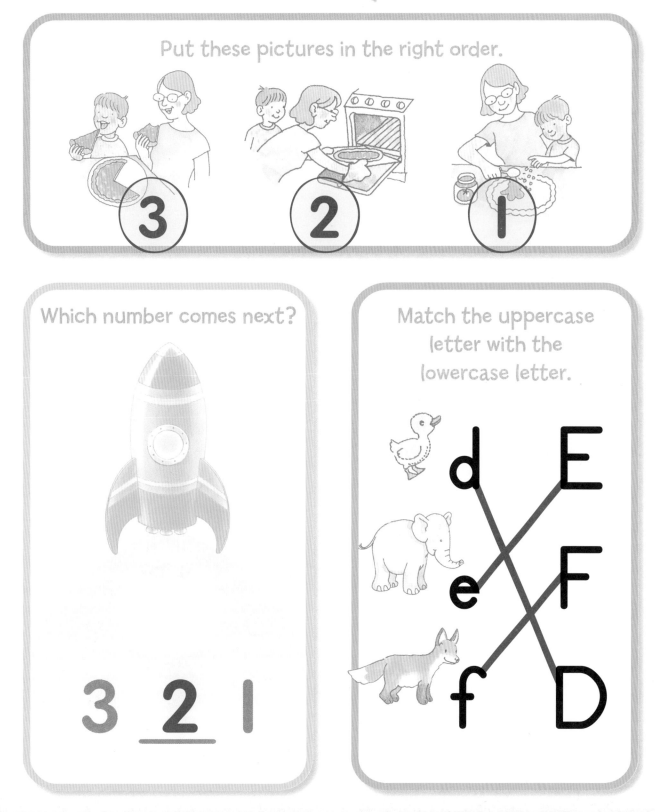

Which number comes next?

3 2 <u>2</u> 1

Match the uppercase letter with the lowercase letter.

Answers for page 6

Which animal lives underwater?

octopus

How many flowers?

17

Which of these vehicles begins with the letter **V**?

van

Which sign shows the number twelve?

$7 $12 $15

Which uppercase and lowercase letters are missing?

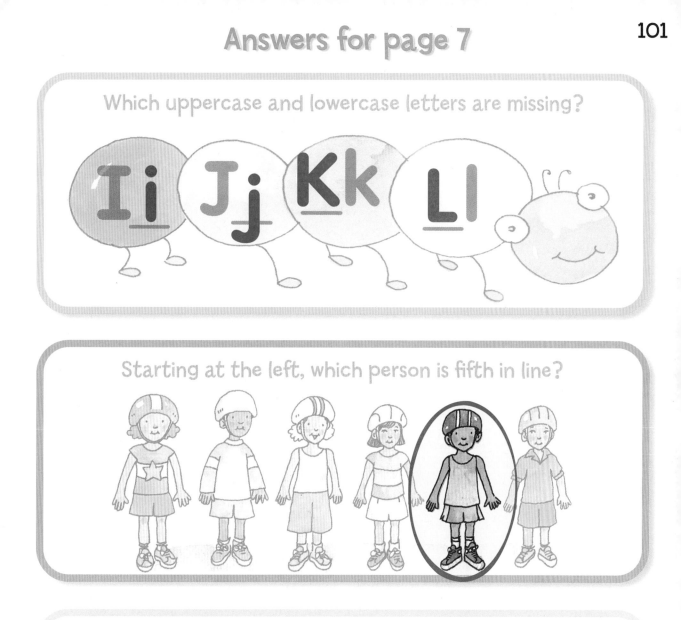

Starting at the left, which person is fifth in line?

How many words in this sentence start with the letter **B**?

My **best buddy Bob** missed the **bus** to the **big baseball** game, so he ran **back** home and **biked** his way over.

8

Answers for page 8

Starting from the left, which fish is third?

Which letters are missing?

A B C D E F G H I

J K L M N O P Q

R S T U V W X Y Z

Put these pictures in the right order.

3

1

2

How many fruits do you see during snack time?

apple

banana

banana

7

apple

pear

apple

orange

How many party hats are in this picture?

9

Answers for page 10

Do you eat dinner before or **after** school?

What is this picture?
What is its first letter?

<u>r</u> ake

Which number comes next?

15 16 <u>17</u>

Which of these animals begins with the letter **C**?

cat

How many umbrellas are in this picture?

10

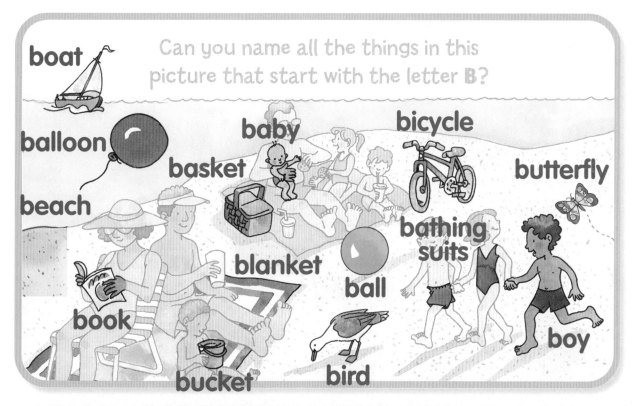

Can you name all the things in this picture that start with the letter **B**?

boat

balloon

baby

bicycle

basket

butterfly

beach

bathing suits

blanket

book

ball

boy

bucket

bird

Answers for page 12

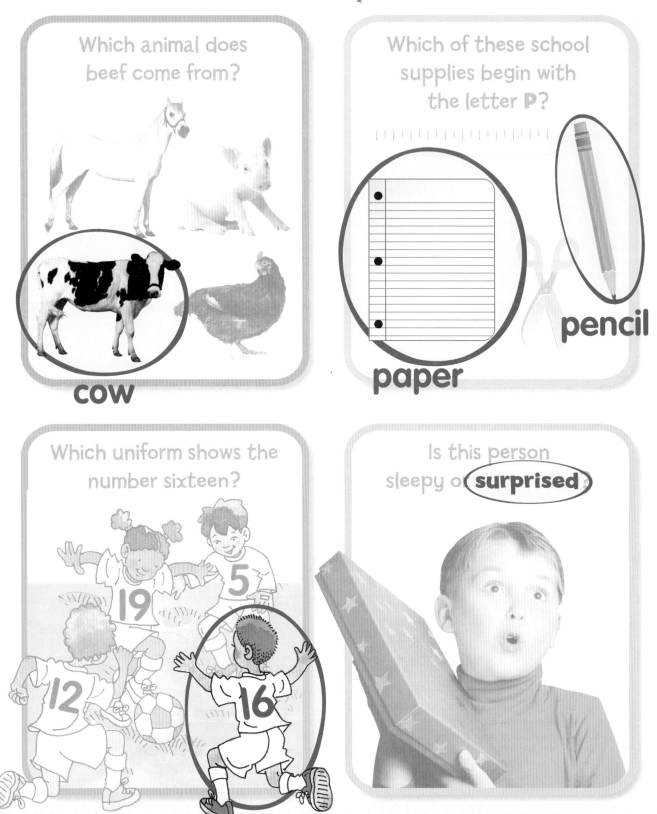

Which animal does beef come from?

cow

Which of these school supplies begin with the letter P?

paper

pencil

Which uniform shows the number sixteen?

Is this person sleepy or **surprised**?

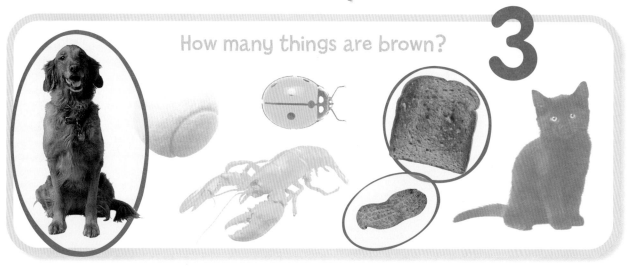

How many things are brown?

3

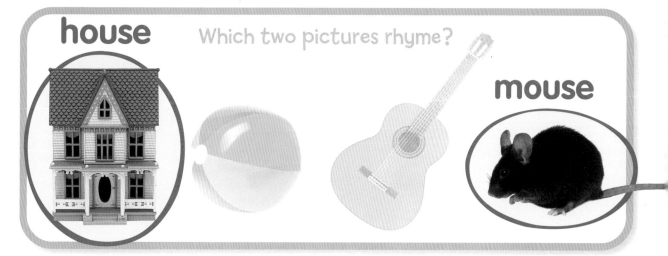

house

Which two pictures rhyme?

mouse

7

How many words in this sentence start with the letter **S**?

While we were at the **seashore** last **Sunday**, we **stopped swimming** to **skip** along the beach and collect **shells** that had washed up on the **sand**.

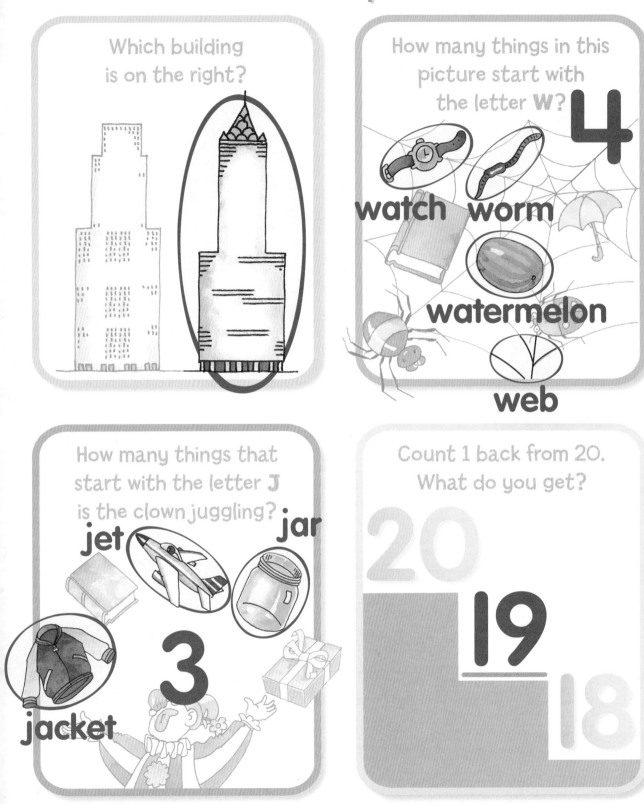

Which building is on the right?

How many things in this picture start with the letter **W**? **4**

watch worm

watermelon

web

How many things that start with the letter **J** is the clown juggling?

jet jar

3

jacket

Count 1 back from 20. What do you get?

20

19

18

How many pictures on this quilt start with the letter Q?

5

quilt
quarter
queen
quail
question mark

How many things are yellow?

3

What number comes next?

14

13
12

Which dominoes have the same number of dots?

9
8
8

Answers for page 16

How many things in this nest start with the letter **N**?

4

nine

nut

nail

noodle

What does the Spanish word "si" mean?

yes

no

hello

How many things in this picture start with the letter **S**?

sailboat

sun

8

sea

sand castle

shell

shovel

seagull

sand

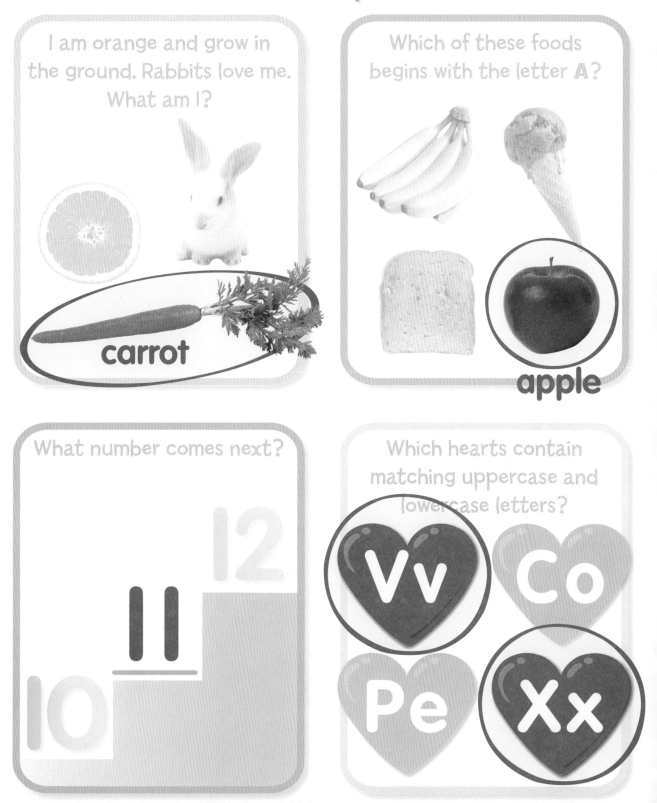

I am orange and grow in the ground. Rabbits love me. What am I?

carrot

Which of these foods begins with the letter **A**?

apple

What number comes next?

12

11

10

Which hearts contain matching uppercase and lowercase letters?

Vv

Co

Pe

Xx

Answers for page 18

I have wrinkly skin and a hard shell,
and I hatch from an egg. Which animal am I?

turtle

Put these pictures in
the right order.

2

1

3

Follow the path with
the pictures that start
with the letter **F**.

Start

Finish

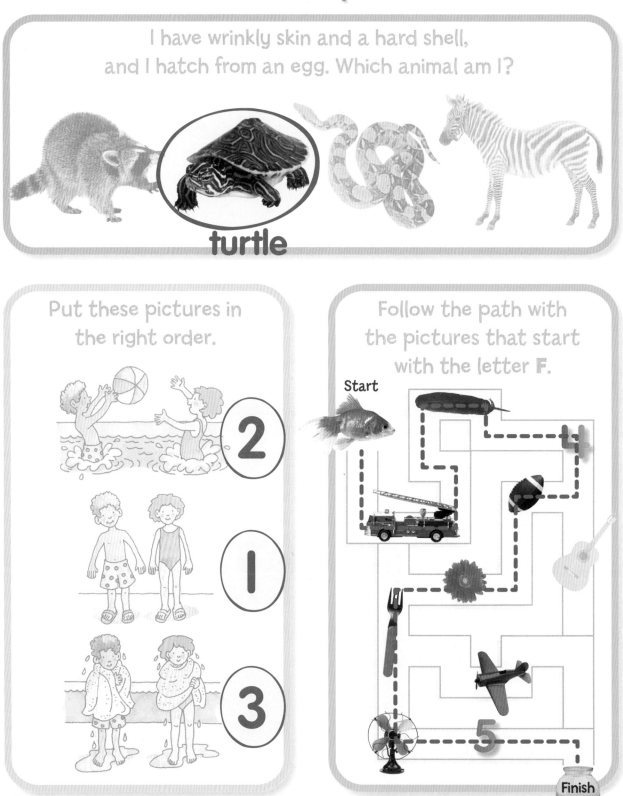

How many monkeys are in this picture?

7

Point to all the things in this picture that start with **F.**

fan

2

flippers

five **5**

frog

fork

fish

What month is Presidents' Day in?

April

February

June

October

Which two pictures rhyme?

hat

cat

Match the animal to the tracks it made.

Which one is used to put out fires?

fire extinguisher

Match the lowercase stamp to the uppercase letter.

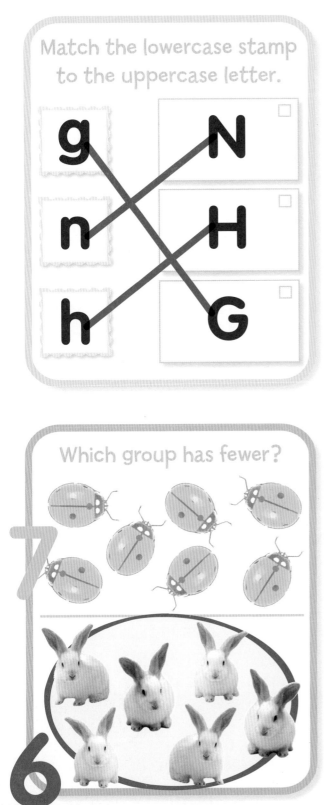

g

n

h

N

H

G

How many words in this sentence start with the letter Q?

5

The **quality** of the **queen's quilt** was **quite** good for the price of one shiny **quarter**.

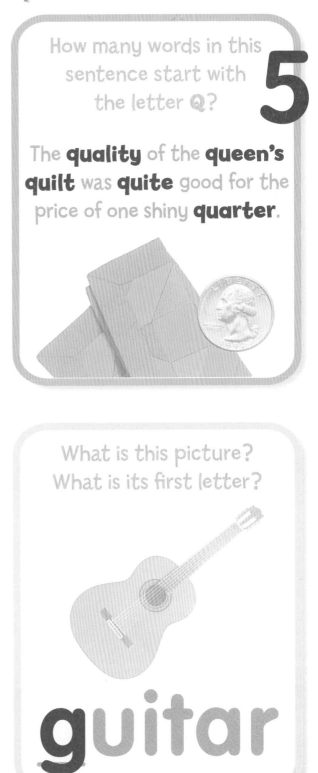

Which group has fewer?

7

6

What is this picture? What is its first letter?

guitar

Which ball contains matching uppercase and lowercase letters?

Qq   Bd   Mn   Yp

What is this picture? What is its first letter?

lion

Count 2 back from 10. What do you get?

10   9   **8**

What does the Spanish word "gracias" mean?

please

what

thank you

Which of these things begins with the letter **T**?

train

Count the rubber ducks.

12

How many things in this picture start with the letter **D**?

4

duck

dog

dragonfly

doll

Answers for page 24

I am yellow and you peel me before eating. Monkeys like me. What am I?

bananas

Match the uppercase letter with the lowercase letter.

K
L
T
t
k
l

Which of these objects begins with the letter B?

bat

Is this child sad or **scared**?

Put these pictures in the right order.

2

1

3

Which of these toys begins with the letter **y**?

yo-yo

What is this picture? What is its first letter?

pig

Answers for page 26

What number comes next?

8 9 10

Match the uppercase letter with the lowercase letter.

G — y
R — g
Y — r

Point to all the things in this picture that start with the letter **C**.

coat

clock

clown

cupcake

cars

cat

cup

Which of these things begin with the letter K?

kite

kangaroo

Which animal crossed the finish line first?

mouse

Which of these clothes begins with the letter G?

glove

I have sharp teeth, scaly skin, and can swim in water or walk on land. Which am I?

alligator

Answers for page 28

How many yellow flowers?

20

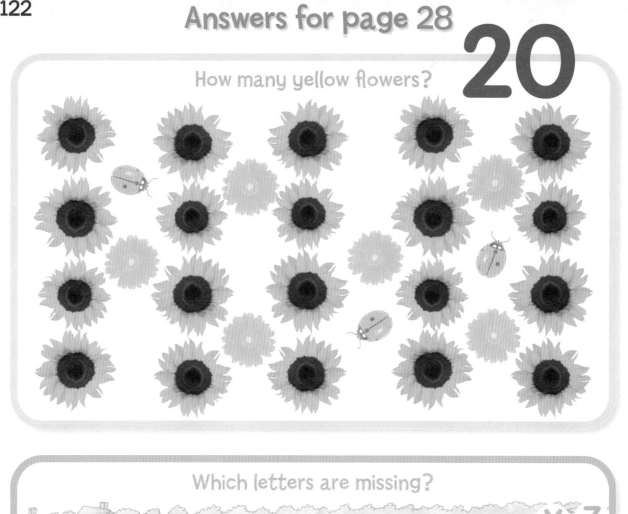

Which letters are missing?

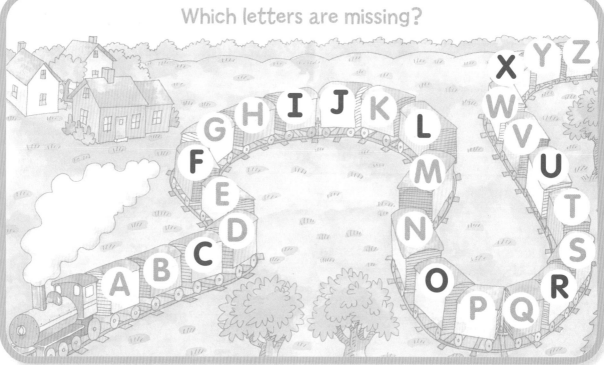

Are there more **seashells** or shovels?

14

12

I live in Africa, have stripes, and am part of the horse family. Which animal am I?

zebra

Count 1 back from 5. What do you get?

5

4

3

Which two pictures rhyme?

frog

dog

Answers for page 30

Put these pictures in the right order.

Count the tigers. Which word tells how many?

Six **(Seven)**

What color are most of the leaves on this tree?

green

Which bugs have the same number of legs?

6

Which sign is an octagon?

STOP

Which pictures on the front page of the paper start with the letter **P**?

piano

pig

What does the Spanish word "adios" mean?

welcome

good-bye

hello

Answers for page 32

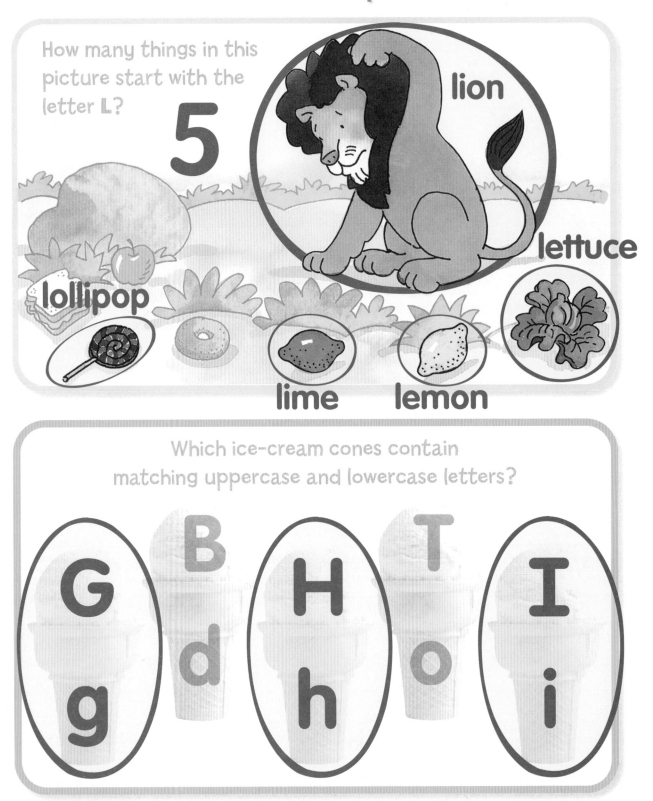

How many things in this picture start with the letter L?

5

lion

lettuce

lollipop

lime

lemon

Which ice-cream cones contain matching uppercase and lowercase letters?

G
g

B
d

H
h

T
o

I
i

Find all the hidden **Z** words at the zoo.

zero

zigzag

zipper

ZOO

zebra

Answers for page 34

Which pizza is divided equally into two halves?

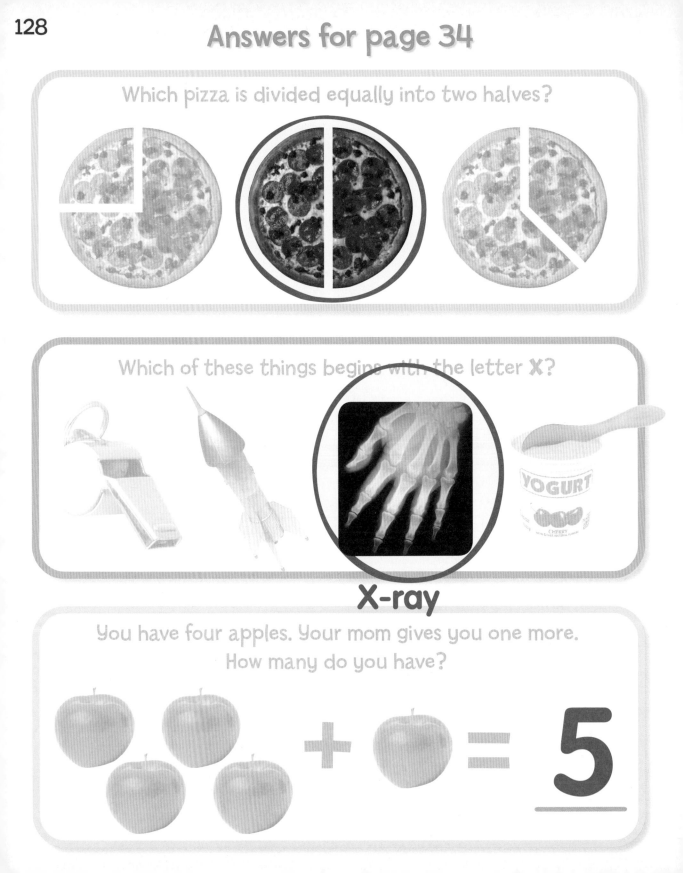

Which of these things begins with the letter **X**?

X-ray

You have four apples. Your mom gives you one more.
How many do you have?

+ **=** **5**

What does the Spanish word "hola" mean?

hot

help

hello

What do you wear to stay safe while biking?

helmet

Match the uppercase and lowercase letters.

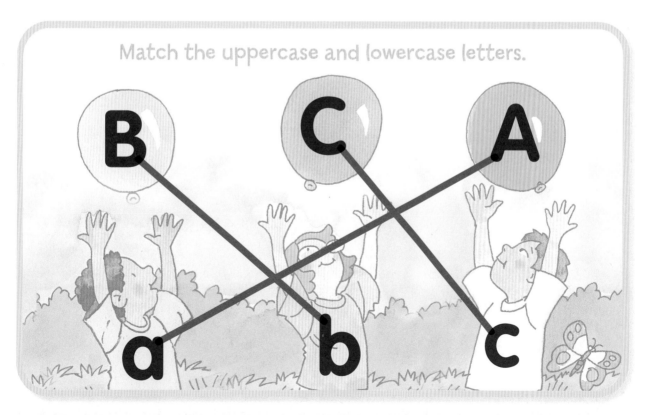

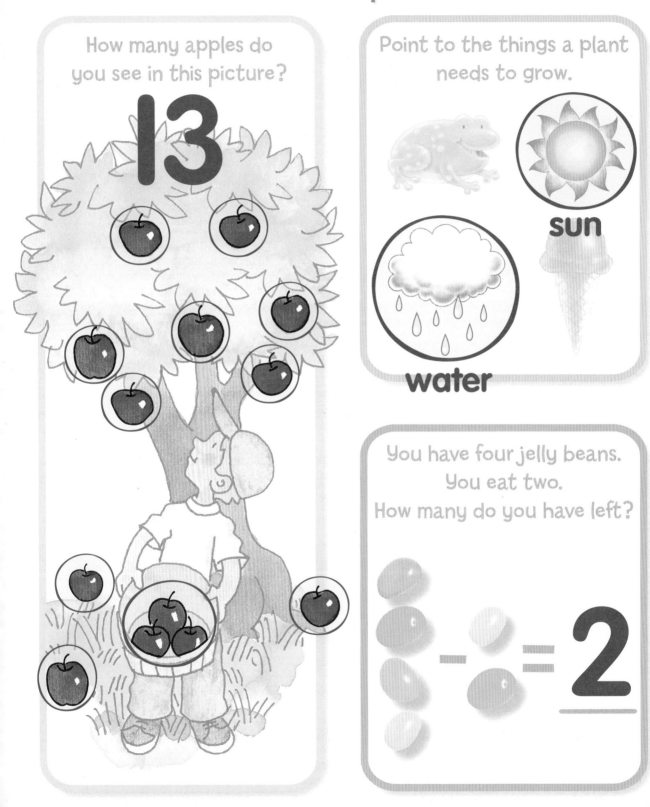

How many apples do you see in this picture?

13

Point to the things a plant needs to grow.

sun

water

You have four jelly beans.
You eat two.
How many do you have left?

- = 2

8

How many things are green?

turtle

fish

chalkboard

book

table

stool

block

truck

Answers for page 38

Which fireman will be second down the pole?

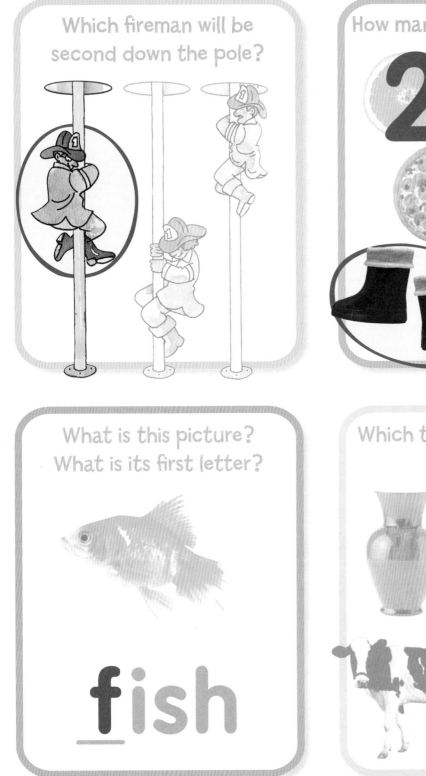

How many pairs do you see?

2

What is this picture? What is its first letter?

_fish

Which two pictures rhyme?

car

star

Answers for page 39

Match the lowercase letter with the uppercase letter.

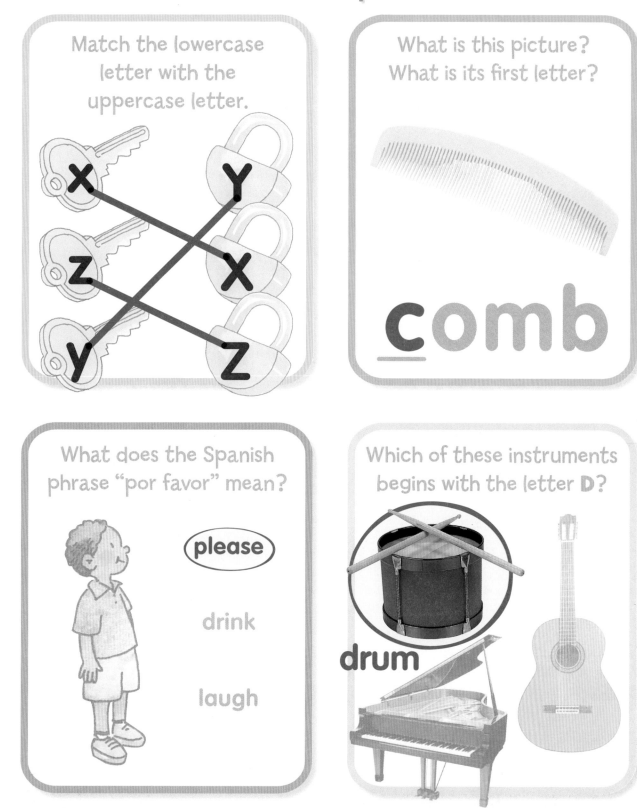

x
z
y

Y
X
Z

What is this picture? What is its first letter?

comb

What does the Spanish phrase "por favor" mean?

(please)

drink

laugh

Which of these instruments begins with the letter **D**?

drum

Answers for page 40

Count the parrots. Which word tells how many?

Seven **(Eight)**

How many things are purple?

2

Read the poem, then find the rhyming words in the picture.

I have a **cat**
who sits on a **mat**.
He ate cookies and **cake**
in the sand by the **lake**.
He liked to lie in the **sun**;
now he's so big, he can't even **run**.

sun

lake

run   cake

Which person is on the right?

Finish the pattern.

day, night,

day, night,

day, **night**

How many circles?

There are five fish in the aquarium. You add three more. How many are there?

Answers for page 42

Choose the picture that rhymes with the underlined word.

The **duck** flew over the **truck**.

Which word in this sentence should have a capital letter?

Bobby likes chocolate cupcakes.

There are seven frogs. Two of them hop away. How many are left?

$-$ $= 5$

Which tool would you use to see things up close?

magnifying glass

Which suitcase is full?

Which one doesn't belong?

insect

What shape is the planet Earth?

cube   cylinder   **sphere**

What does the French word "oui" mean?

yes

no

hello

Answers for page 44

One sock is missing its mate.
Which pattern is missing?

Put the letters together.
What word is this?

What do you get when
you mix **yellow** and **red**?

orange

Uniform starts with a
long **U** sound. Which person
is wearing a uniform?

Counting backward, which number is missing?

8 7 6 5 4

Which of these is not a rectangle?

circle

Which animal rhymes with chair?

bear

Answers for page 46

Are there more horses inside or **outside** the pen?

6

7

Which person is last in line
for a turn on the slide?

What part of the boat
is a triangle?

sail

Which tool measures time?

clock

Can you find 5 things
wrong in this picture?

Answers for page 48

Which letter is missing?
Use the picture
to help you decide.

b u s

Put the letters together.
What word is this?

SUN

Which dinosaur is biggest?

Which ball gets tossed
through the hoop?

basketball

Read the sentence. Choose the picture
that rhymes with the underlined word.

I tried to feed the **goat** some corn, but it ate my hat instead.

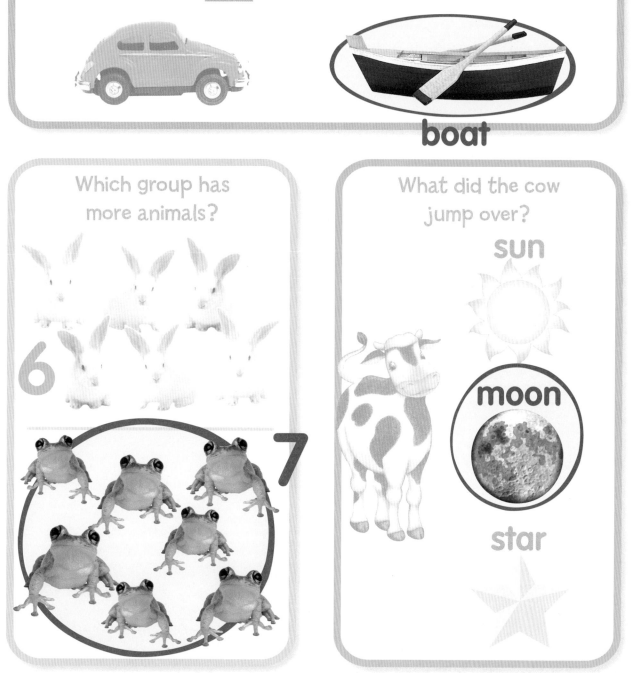

boat

Which group has
more animals?

6

7

What did the cow
jump over?

sun

moon

star

Answers for page 50

Which object is
in the middle?

flower

Which letter is missing?
Use the picture
to help you decide.

d o g

Which animal is in
front of the barn?

sheep

Which animal is
the chick's mother?

chicken

What flavor comes next? Cherry or **mint**?

What do you get when you mix **red** and blue?

purple

Which one rhymes with clock?

sock

Answers for page 52

There are ten bees. Four of them return to the hive.
How many are left?

$-$ $=$ **6**

Which letter is missing?
Use the picture to
help you decide.

dr**u**m

Which truck is smallest?

Which words should have capital letters?

My good friend **Annie** is moving to a new home by the ocean in **California**.

Fill in the missing letter.

bea**r**

What is another word for an uppercase letter? It starts with this letter.

C

capital

What do you get when you mix **white** and **red**?

pink

Answers for page 54

Which president is on the dollar bill?

George Washington

Which rabbit is above the ground?

Answers for page 56

Which color comes next?

blue

Which butterfly is the same size as this one?

Point to the guitar.

How many words in this sentence start with **G**?

The silly **goose giggled** at the **giant** swan.

3

Which of these is not a triangle?

diamond

Put the letters together. What word is this?

CAT

Fill in the missing letter.

sku**n**k

Answers for page 58

What kind of little animal did Mary have?

piglet

kitten

lamb

calf

Which object is heaviest?

truck

Which season comes after spring?

fall

summer

winter

Point to the girl's elbows.

Fill in the blank.
The children are playing
Duck, **Duck**, Goose.

Which words should have
capital letters?

It was a good idea to let
John play. **He** helped us
win the game!

What color comes next?

yellow

Answers for page 60

Point to the musical instrument.

drum

What did Hansel drop on the ground
to make a trail?

bread crumbs

buttons

string

Which duck is below the boat?

Which one doesn't belong?

strawberry

Which thing rhymes with coat?

boat

Put the letters together. What word is this?

PIG

Which giraffe is tallest?

Answers for page 62

Change the first letter in "map" to get a kind of hat. What letter did you use?

cap

Put the letters together. What word is this?

NET

What did Humpty Dumpty have a great fall off of?

wall

What month is it if we're watching fireworks for Independence Day?

June

July

August

September

Which rock has fewer turtles?

7

5

You've made five ice-cream cones for your friends.
Three more friends come over and you make cones for them.
How many ice-cream cones have you made?

+ = **8**

What did Jack trade his old cow for?

wagon

beans

new cow

Answers for page 64

How many states are there in the USA?

Which ticket line is longer?

Which letter is missing? Use the picture to help you decide.

sh_e_ll

Which words should have capital letters?

On Mondays we have art.

Choose the picture that rhymes with the underlined word.

The black **bat** flew by the scared ___**cat**___.

Which letter is missing? Use the pictures to help you decide.

m

c **a** n

p

Answers for page 66

How many times do you see this pattern  in this picture?

6

What did Rapunzel let down?

hair

rope

vine

Which building is the fire station?

Which rabbits are next to each other?

In *The Tortoise and the Hare,*
who won the race by going slow and steady?

tortoise

hare

snail

Answers for page 68

Put the letters together.
What word is this?

When someone gives you a present, do you feel angry or **happy**?

How many squares?

8

Which planet's name starts with **S**?

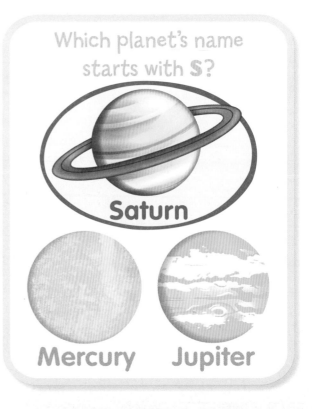

Saturn

Mercury   Jupiter

Change the first letter in "cat" to get a flying animal. What letter did you use?

bat

What do you get when you mix blue and yellow?

green

What do you call your parents' parents?

grandparents

Which one does a car need to run?

gas

Answers for page 70

Which animal is the horse's baby?

colt

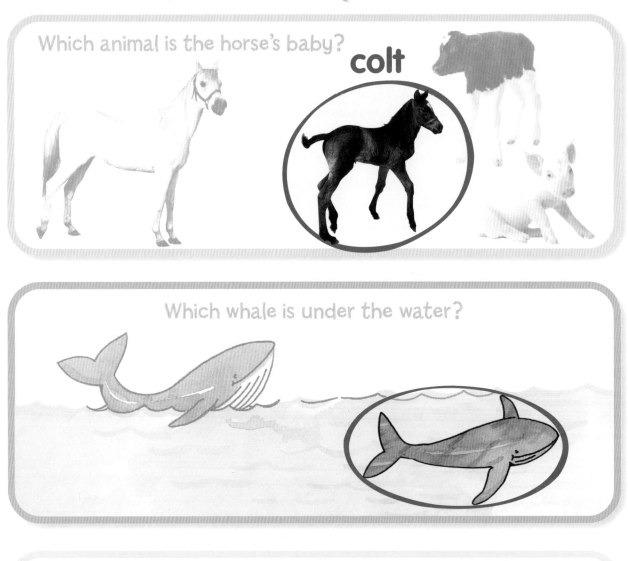

Which whale is under the water?

Where will this bus take the children every morning?

store

school

library

There are two nests with eggs. One nest has seven eggs. The other has four. How many eggs are there?

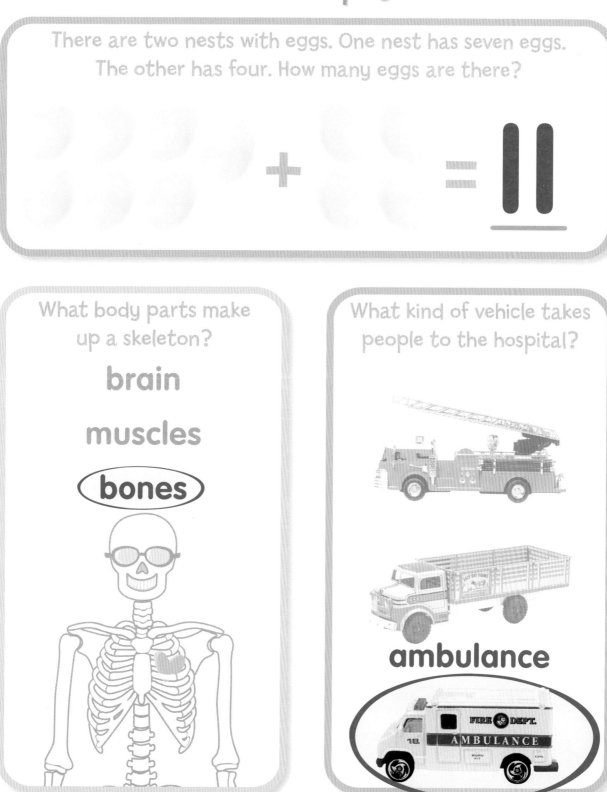

What body parts make up a skeleton?

brain

muscles

bones

What kind of vehicle takes people to the hospital?

ambulance

Answers for page 72

Which one would you
use to stay dry?

umbrella

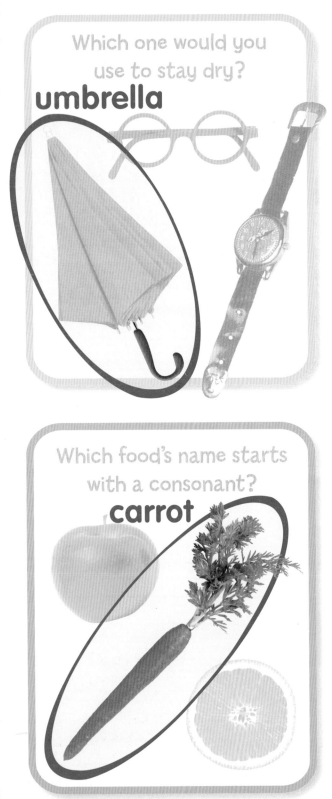

Which letter do you hear
at the end of **fork**?

(**K**) or G

Which food's name starts
with a consonant?

carrot

How many words in this
sentence start with **M**?

The **messy monkeys**
had a **mop**.

3

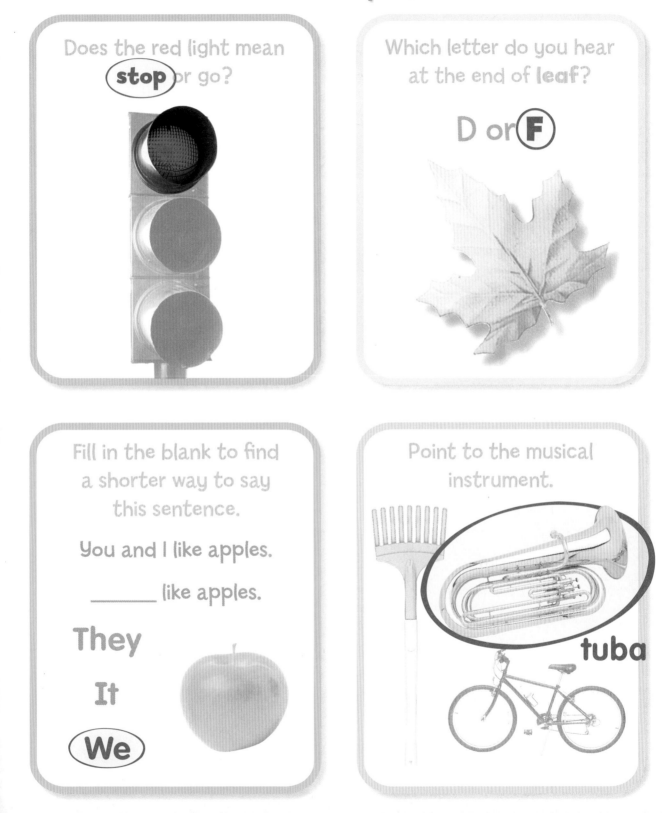

Does the red light mean **stop** or go?

Which letter do you hear at the end of **leaf**?

D or **F**

Fill in the blank to find a shorter way to say this sentence.

You and I like apples.

_____ like apples.

They

It

We

Point to the musical instrument.

tuba

Answers for page 74

What did Rumpelstiltskin spin into gold?

yarn (**straw**) corn

Which activity takes longer — climbing a (**mountain**) or a ladder?

Which tool helps you see in the dark?

flashlight

Answer for page 75

Which items have a hard **C** sound
like you hear in the word "car"?

cup

coat

can

candy

Answers for page 76

What is another way to say "action word"?

noun

verb

adjective

Which tool can be used to measure temperature?

32°

10°

thermometer

What is this mark?

?

exclamation point

comma

question mark

In an emergency, what number do you dial for help?

411

911

800

Which word means "person, place, or thing"?

noun
adjective
adverb

What time is it?

2:00 11:00 **4:00**

Which activity takes longer — reading a **book** or a sign?

EXIT

What word should go on this red sign?

SLOW **STOP** GO

Answers for page 78

Look at the clues. Put them together. What is the word?

+ ⬤ = **snowball**

Which one would you find in **Paris**?

Eiffel Tower

What does a person need to put on before going out into the sun?

sunscreen

Sunscreen Lotion

Which words have the soft **C** sound?

Cindy ate **cereal** in the **center** of her **city**.

How much is this worth?

31¢

Which picture shows something frozen?

ice pop

Point to the buildings in order from shortest to tallest.

2 1 3

Answer for page 80

Which pictures have a long **A**
like you hear in the word "game"?
Follow those pictures from start to finish.

Fill in the blank to find a shorter way to say this sentence.

The girl is skating.

_____ is skating.

He

She

It

What's missing from this bird?

wings

Which pictures have a long I like you hear in the word "ice"?

bicycle

kite

Use the picture to answer the riddle.

What can you put in a bucket to make it lighter?

hole

Answers for page 82

How much are one penny
and one dime worth?

11¢

What do you say when
you want someone
to pass the pizza?

(**please**) / you're welcome

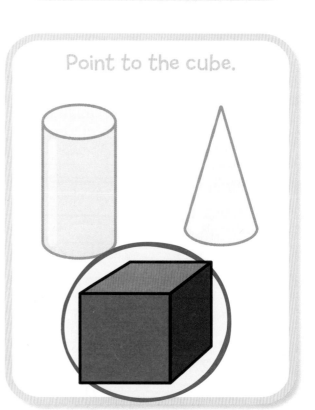

Use the picture to
answer the riddle.

What falls in winter
but never gets hurt?

snow

Point to the cube.

How many things in this picture have the short O sound you hear in the word "octopus"?

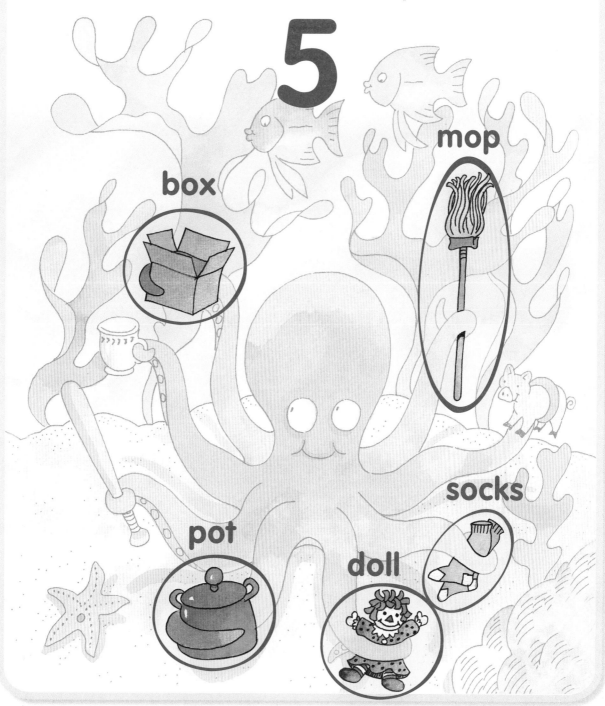

5

box

mop

pot

doll

socks

Answers for page 84

Which person is oldest?

What does an audience
do at the end of
a performance?

clap

What mark do you
put at the end of a
regular sentence?

period •

comma ,

question ?
mark

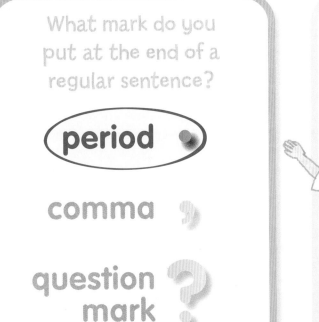

Point to the twins.

What's missing from this van?

wheels

Look at the clues. Put them together. What is the word?

+ = **doghouse**

Answers for page 86

Fill in the blank to find
a shorter way to say
this sentence.

The children are making music.

_____ are making music.

They

Them

It

Which one is the cylinder?

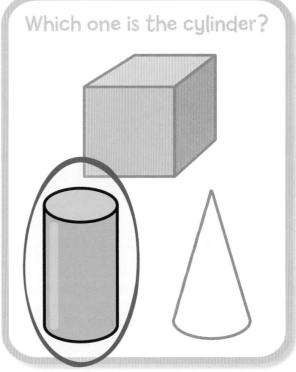

How many of these
things are alive?

flowers

dog

How many months
are there in a year?

20

12

8

10

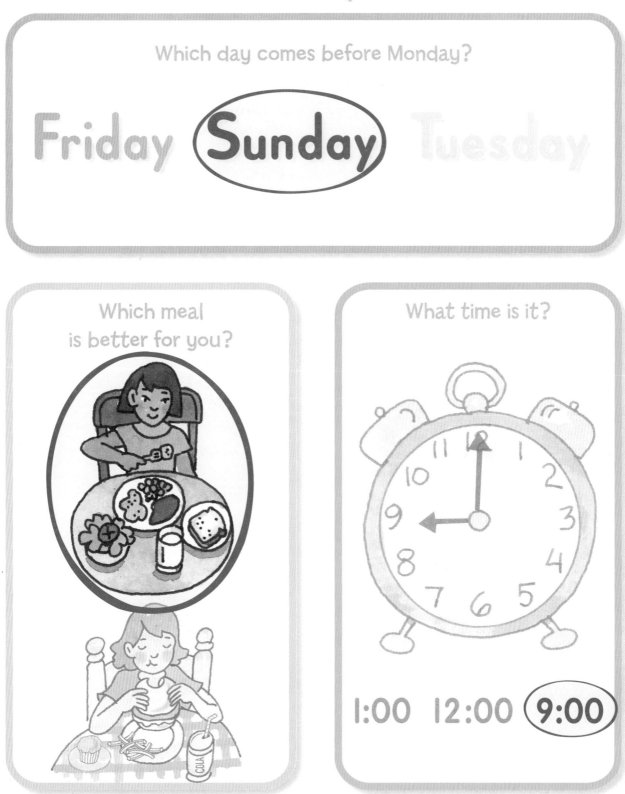

Which day comes before Monday?

Friday **(Sunday)** Tuesday

Which meal is better for you?

What time is it?

1:00 12:00 **(9:00)**

Answers for page 88

Name the 5 senses.

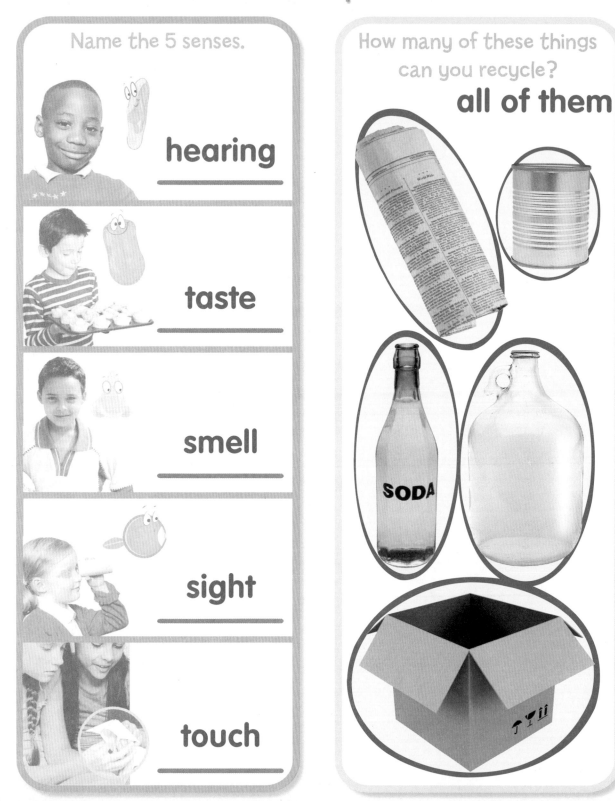

hearing

taste

smell

sight

touch

How many of these things can you recycle?

all of them

SODA

Look at the clues. Put them together. What is the word?

+ ⭕ **=** **baseball**

_____

Which pictures have a long **o** like you hear in the word "boat"?

coat

goat

rope

bone

soap

Answers for page 90

Which one doesn't belong?

pencil

Point to the plant's roots.

Which item can you buy with two dimes?

20¢

35¢

Which word in this sentence describes something?

Jack picked a **pretty** flower.

It's an adjective.

What happens second?

What body part is the squirrel missing?

tail

What is the better one to say when you need to get by someone?

excuse me / I'm sorry

Answers for page 92

Which pictures start with a soft **G** like the word "gym"?

giraffe

gingerbread

What is the opposite of wet?

dry

hot

sticky

Which picture shows a windy day?

What time is it?

9:00   11:00   7:00

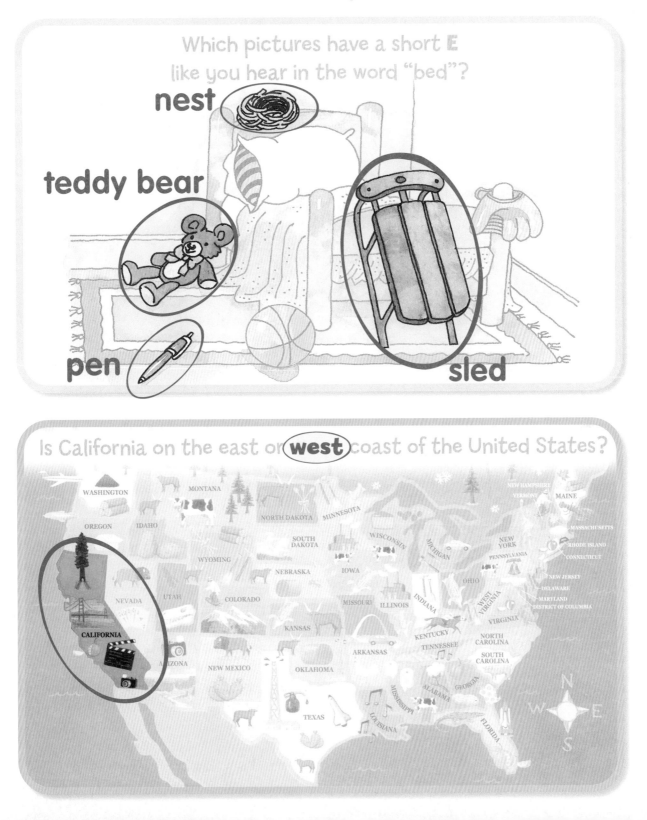

Which pictures have a short **E**
like you hear in the word "bed"?

nest

teddy bear

pen

sled

Is California on the east or **west** coast of the United States?

Answers for page 94

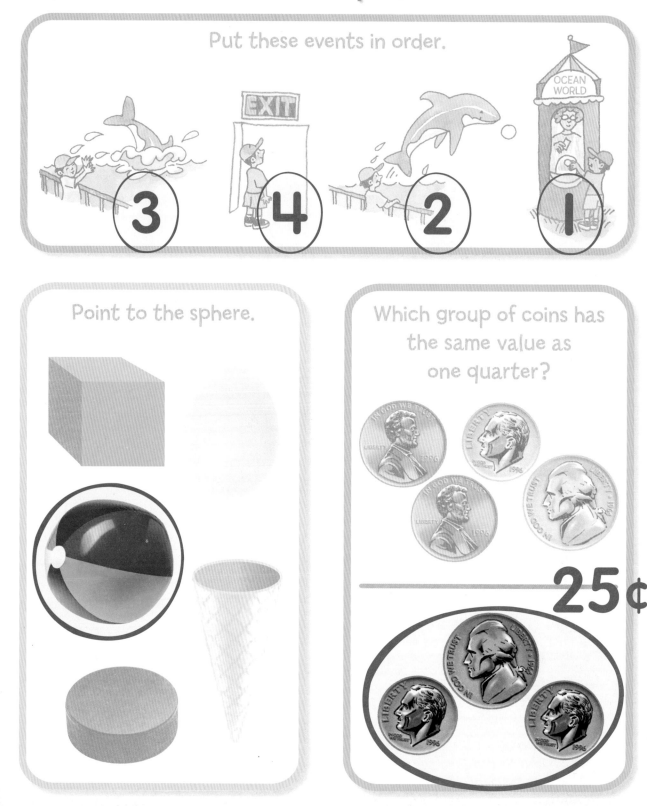

Put these events in order.

3   4   2   1

Point to the sphere.

Which group of coins has the same value as one quarter?

25¢

Answers for page 96

Which of these pictures have a hard **G** as in "girl"?

goat   **glove**

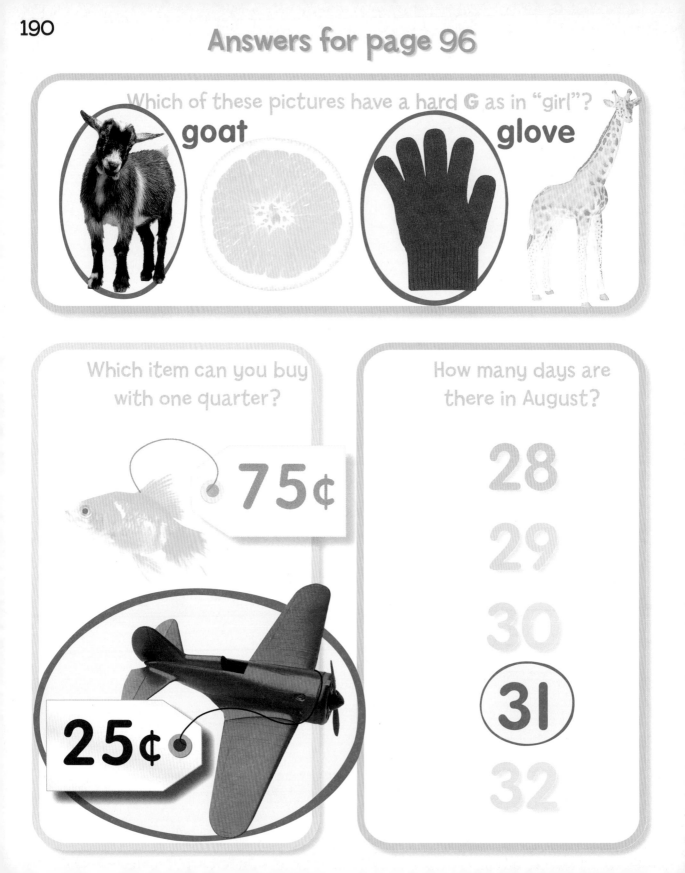

Which item can you buy with one quarter?

75¢

25¢

How many days are there in August?

28

29

30

(31)

32

Can you buy this item with two quarters?

no

$1.00

You have twelve toy soldiers. You give a friend six.
How many do you have left?

= **6**

Can you buy this item with two quarters?

no

$1.00

You have twelve toy soldiers. You give a friend six.
How many do you have left?

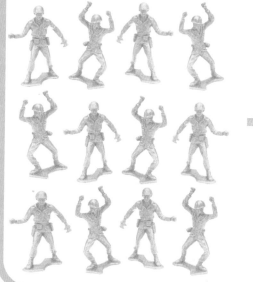 − = **6**